MARSHAL LAW

FEAR AND LOATHING

Originally published in magazine
form as MARSHAL LAW #1-6.
Published by Epic Comics
387 Park Avenue South
New York, NY 10016

ISBN #0-87135-676-7
First Printing June 1990
10 9 8 7 6 5 4 3 2 1

writer/creator
PAT MILLS

artist/creator
KEVIN O'NEILL

letterer
PHIL FELIX

editor
DANIEL CHICHESTER

re-print editor
MARIE JAVINS
MARGARET CLARK

executive editor
CARL POTTS

editor in chief
TOM DeFALCO

I read somewhere this story about the great Japanese artist Hokusai. At work on an illustration for a pillow book, which depicted, as do all such *shunga*, the art of procreation rendered in the most unabashed detail, the master print-maker was approached by one of his students. The young man enquired as to why the male anatomy was drawn so violently out of proportion, exaggerated to the point of being grotesque. Hokusai replied, very simply, that the actual subject was a piddling thing, and would seem insignificant in his scheme were it not re-invented, flattered and inflamed.

From Hokusai to Mills and O'Neill? Why not? They show a similar disregard for the restraints of realism; a similar passion for searing an image and an idea onto your mind's eye (*eye's mind*, perhaps?); a way of recreating the world so that it becomes a vary particular vision. Strong meat. Unlike Hokusai; whose subject in the *shunga* was loving sexual contact, Mills and O'Neill are creating stories of mayhem and corruption, in which the monster and the hero become virtually interchangeable.

This ambiguity of role is not, of course, new. There seems to have been a spate of comic books recently that have inverted the pat dichotomies upon which most super-hero stories are based. Some of these paradoxes have even touched the intellectual sand-box of the movies, though not with sufficient force to slow the sale of popcorn.

Marshal Law, however, marks a new extreme in this revisioning. A purifying self-consciousness is upon the work. It refuses to be ignorant of its significance (which regrettably so much *fantastique*, whether in prose or pictures, or both, is). It allows us to see the grotesquery of the masque. Heroes and heroines pumped to ridiculous tumescence. Gleaming icons acting out the dope-fiend Freud's worst nightmares in the sky above our heads.

But the narrative is cunningly constructed, and the images presented with such wit, that we are denied many of the pleasures such post-apocalyptic sprees covertly offer. The sadistic, sexist, brutal world of *Marshal Law* doesn't have this reader panting with vicarious satisfaction. O'Neill's style is anti-sensual, stressing the absurdity of these demi-deities rather then any erotic appeal. Nor does the violence excite. This is not the Bam Pow School of Fisticuffs, in which the reader is the hero's invisible buddy, at the heart of the battle with him. We watch the blood-letting remotely, the posture of the fighters oddly stilted, the frames rife with repulsive detail. We close the final page disgusted and distressed.

If none of their seems to be a recommendation then I heartily suggest you ask your dealer to provide something more conventional. There's a lot of it to chose from, as long as you can tell one title from the next. Personally, though reading *Marshal Law* is not precisely a pleasure, it will leave a mark on my imagination the way countless pleasures have failed to do. And from its pessimism there is no way out but up, which is perversely perhaps, a kind of hope. I applaud both creators for their artistry and integrity, and look forward—not without a little trepidation to a Pillow Book from Mills and O'Neill to encourage the repopulation of their imaginary wasteland.

Clive Barker, London
1st May 1990

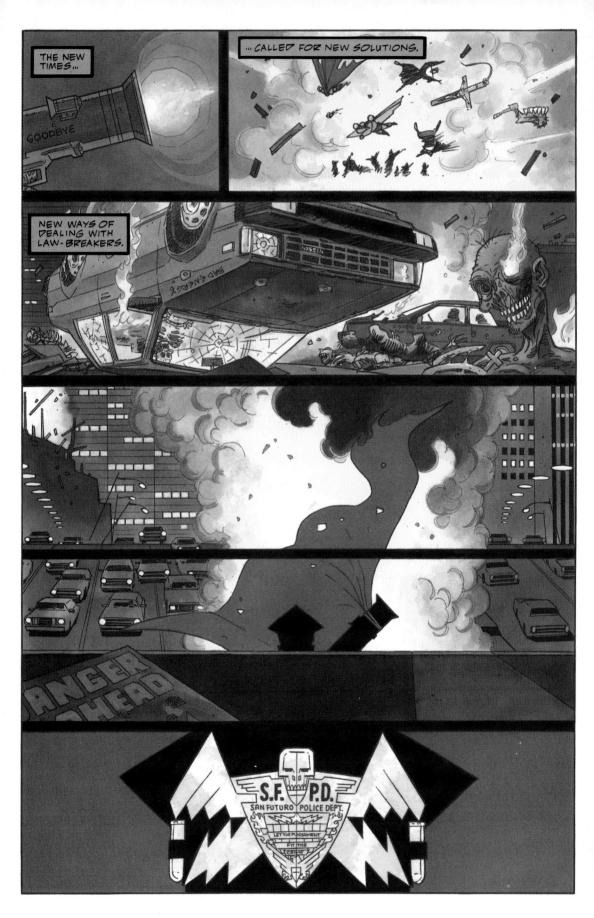

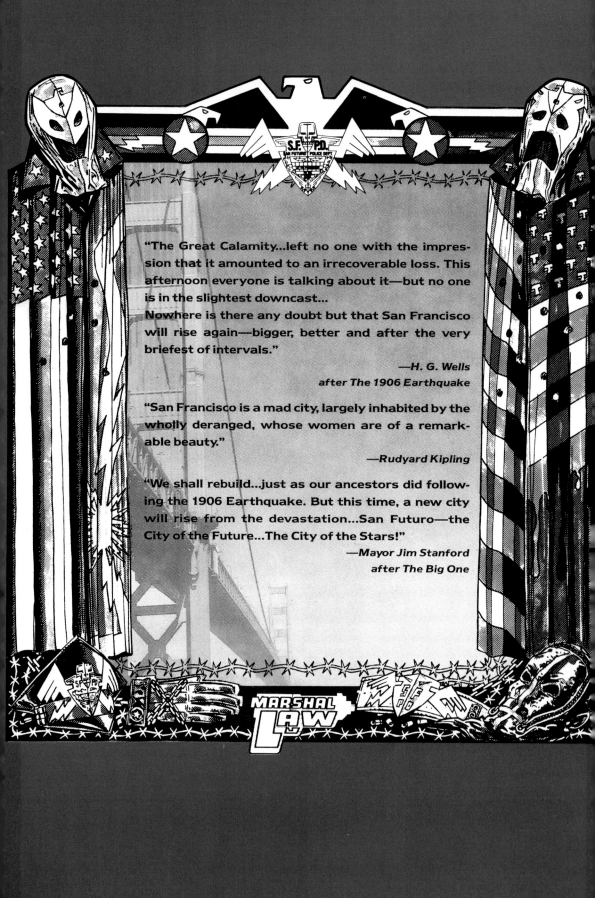

"The Great Calamity...left no one with the impression that it amounted to an irrecoverable loss. This afternoon everyone is talking about it—but no one is in the slightest downcast...
Nowhere is there any doubt but that San Francisco will rise again—bigger, better and after the very briefest of intervals."

—H. G. Wells
after *The 1906 Earthquake*

"San Francisco is a mad city, largely inhabited by the wholly deranged, whose women are of a remarkable beauty."

—Rudyard Kipling

"We shall rebuild...just as our ancestors did following the 1906 Earthquake. But this time, a new city will rise from the devastation...San Futuro—the City of the Future...The City of the Stars!"

—Mayor Jim Stanford
after *The Big One*

MARSHAL LAW

"Masked men appeared openly in the streets and garrotted citizens, apparently defying law or resistance. The police hardly dared enter there except in a numerous, strongly armed company."

"Midnight assaults ending in murder were common. There were usually two murders a day, arson was frequent, prostitution and its earnings a way of life, robbery a spectator sport."

"It was evident that the offenders defied and laughed at all the puny efforts of the authorities to control them. No decent man or woman was safe to walk the streets after dark. People generally carried, during all hours, loaded firearms about their persons."

FOUND DISPOSING OF BODY

RAN FROM THE SCENE

SWALLOWED HARD WHEN ASKED IF HE WAS THE SLEEPMAN.

LOOKED PALE

LOOKED NERVOUS

LOOKED GUILTY

GMMMGG

WAS THAT A MUMBLE OF GUILT?

NO?

YES?

NO?

PRISONER NODDED HE WAS GUILTY.

NOW WE'RE GETTING TO THE TRUTH OF THE MATTER.

AND FOR THE FINAL PROOF

PULL HIS TIGHTS DOWN.

NO ... NO MONKEY JOKES IF YOU PLEASE. THIS IS SERIOUS BUSINESS. THIS OFFENDS MY EYE. THIS IS NOT NICE.

NUKE ME SLOWLY

THIS IS GIVING US SUPER HEROES A BAD NAME!

"Law it appeared was but a non-entity to be scoffed at. Redress could be had for aggression but through the never failing remedy so admirably laid down in the code of Judge Lynch. Let each man be his own executioner. Fie upon your laws!"

— Quotes from *Annals of San Francisco, Metropolitan Life Unveiled, or The Mysteries and Miseries of American Great Cities*, and other 19th Century sources.

CAN'T STAY HERE, I'LL TAKE YOU TO "THE MIDNIGHT."

I GET TO RIDE IN THE EAGLE? WOW! I'LL GET MY THINGS!

MAYBE THAT'S WHY I LIKE VULNERABLE PEOPLE ... PEOPLE WITH PROBLEMS.

PEOPLE WHO AREN'T GODDAM PERFECT.

I'VE SOUVENIRS OF ALL THE SUPER HEROES -- IT'S MY HOBBY, YOU KNOW ...

ALL THE FAMOUS ONES ...

ENLIST

...BACK TO THE SCREAMING EAGLES IN THE ZONE, THEY WERE THE GREATEST.

A land fit for SUPER HEROES

THEY WERE ...

FROM THE PANAMA CANAL ZONE TO THE AMAZON JUNGLE, IT WAS KNOWN SIMPLY AS "THE ZONE."

TO MEN NOT AFRAID TO DIE ...

BECAUSE THEY ARE ALREADY DEAD.

CAPTAIN CURFEW! ARE YOU TEAMING UP WITH MARSHAL LAW NOW?

NOT EXACTLY... "HOSEDOWN IN A PUBLIC PLACE."

HUH?

FLYING FLASHER.

TOLD YOU, MARSHAL -- I *HAD* TO GO.

AND WITH THE PRACTICAL PROBLEMS OF WEARING YOUR UNDERWEAR *OVER* YOUR TIGHTS...

SHUT IT, PIGEON.

THE SLEEPMAN COULD BE A "SURP"--A SURPLUS HERO DRIVEN CRAZY BY THE ZONE. IT WAS ONE EXPLANATION THAT FITTED. THE ONE THEY WANTED UP-TOWN IN SAN FUTURO.

SO FAR HE'D MURDERED TWO STRIPPERGRAMS AND THREE SLEEP-EEZIES... ALL DRESSED LIKE *CELESTE.*

ONLY A FEW SUPER HEROES, LIKE THE *PUBLIC SPIRIT,* COULD FLY...

THAT WAS THE *REAL* REASON HE WAS ENGAGED TO CELESTE... THE SIRENS WERE SECRET AGENTS WITH SUPER SEXUAL POWERS...

BUT MAYBE SHE WAS STILL NOT ENOUGH...

BUT AUTOPSIES ON THE BODIES--BLOOD AND SEMEN SAMPLES--SUGGESTED HE WAS A *FLYER*... THEIR SUPERHUMAN METABOLISM MADE A SEXUAL RELATIONSHIP WITH AN ORDINARY WOMAN HIGHLY DANGEROUS ...

THERE WERE STORIES ABOUT THE PUBLIC SPIRIT'S WILD PARTIES AT SAN SIMEON-- THE CASTLE PRESENTED TO HIM BY A GRATEFUL NATION ... HIS INSATIABLE APPETITE ...

REASON ENOUGH TO MAKE HIM A SUSPECT ... BESIDES ... I DIDN'T LIKE THE CUT OF HIS TRUNKS.

THE OFFICIAL EXPLANATION FOR *THE BIG ONE*-- THE MEGAQUAKE THAT TOOK OUT SAN FRANCISCO--WAS THE JUPITER EFFECT ... THE TIDAL PULL OF THE PLANETS ON THE SAN ANDREAS FAULT.

60,000 BUILDINGS WERE DESTROYED AND 8 SQUARE MILES OF THE CITY. THE QUAKE MEASURED 9 ON THE RICHTER SCALE, HITTING THE CITY WITH A FORCE 300,000 TIMES THAT OF THE HIROSHIMA BOMB.

THE TIDAL WAVE THAT FOLLOWED HURLED SHIPS INLAND, LEAVING THE U.S. AIRCRAFT CARRIER JOHN PAUL JONES STRADDLING THE FREEWAYS. THEN CAME THE FIRE ... AND THE DEATH CLOUD FROM DIABLO CANYON NUCLEAR PLANT ...

YOU COULDN'T MEASURE THE HUMAN MISERY...

DANNY WILL BE OKAY. I'LL LOOK AFTER HIM.

SEWER SIDES ARE UP!

CAVE-COPS...THAT'S WHAT THEY CALL US WHEN WE WORK OUT OF SECRET POLICE PRECINCTS ...

MINE'S THE BART-- BAY AREA RAPID TRANSPORT-- STATION UNDER WHAT USED TO BE HALLIDIE PLAZA.

I USE SEVERAL ROUND-ABOUT ROUTES TO IT.

I DON'T ENCOURAGE VISITORS.

BETTER LUCK IN HELL

WE SHOULD HAVE KNOWN BETTER

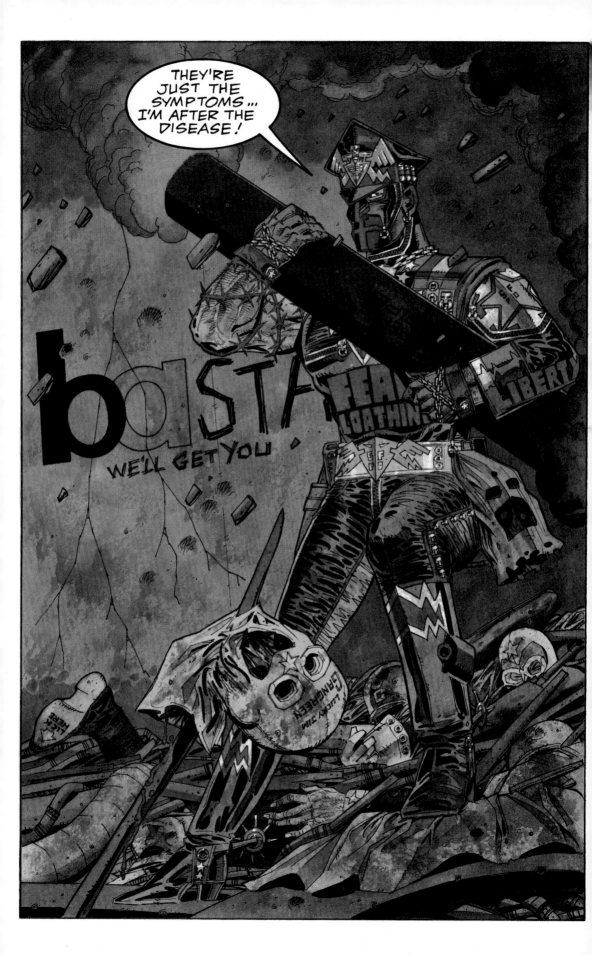

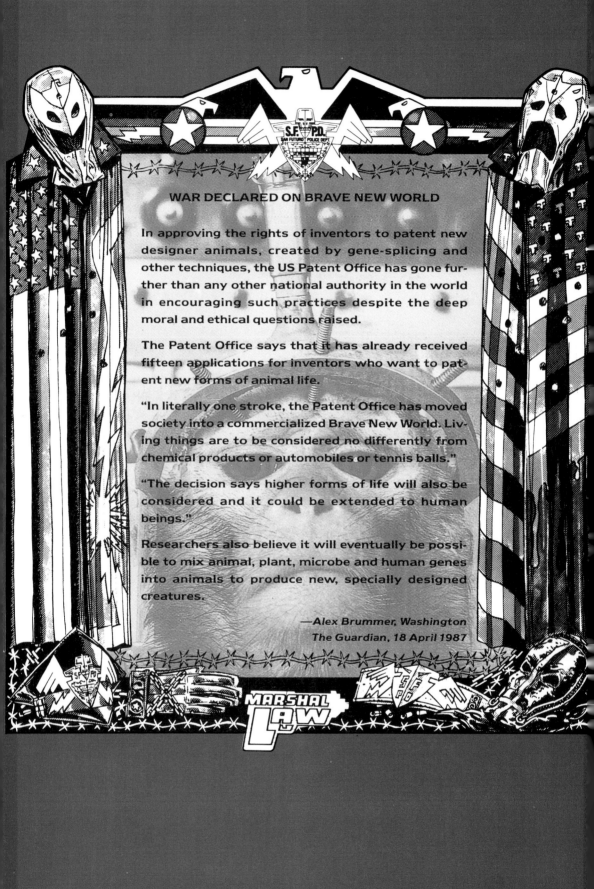

WAR DECLARED ON BRAVE NEW WORLD

In approving the rights of inventors to patent new designer animals, created by gene-splicing and other techniques, the US Patent Office has gone further than any other national authority in the world in encouraging such practices despite the deep moral and ethical questions raised.

The Patent Office says that it has already received fifteen applications for inventors who want to patent new forms of animal life.

"In literally one stroke, the Patent Office has moved society into a commercialized Brave New World. Living things are to be considered no differently from chemical products or automobiles or tennis balls."

"The decision says higher forms of life will also be considered and it could be extended to human beings."

Researchers also believe it will eventually be possible to mix animal, plant, microbe and human genes into animals to produce new, specially designed creatures.

—Alex Brummer, Washington
The Guardian, 18 April 1987

THEN CAINE WAS SENT ON HIS MISSION TO THE NEAREST STAR: OUR SUN'S DARK COMPANION STAR *NEMESIS.*

TRAVELLING CLOSE TO THE SPEED OF LIGHT, THE ROUND TRIP HAD TAKEN *TWO YEARS* ...

WHILE, DUE TO EINSTEIN'S THEORY OF RELATIVITY, *A QUARTER OF A CENTURY* WENT BY ON EARTH.

BUT THE MOST INTERESTING BITS IN THE REPORT WERE

THE MISSING BITS

IN ALL THAT LYING BULLSHIT.

I HOPE YOU'LL FIND IT OF USE, MARSHAL?

IT LEFT TOO MANY QUESTIONS UNANSWERED ABOUT AN "ACCIDENT" TWENTY FIVE YEARS AGO.

FORTUNATELY, THE SUPERSTAR WAS HOLDING A PANEL *ANSWERING* QUESTIONS FROM HIS DEVOTED FANS.

I WENT ALONG.

STAND TALL AMERICA!

I- I'LL CONFESS THAT I'VE BEEN A LITTLE AFRAID TO SUGGEST WHAT I'M GOING TO SUGGEST ...

BUT I'M MORE AFRAID NOT TO.

BEFORE WE BEGIN, WILL YOU JOIN WITH ME IN A MINUTE OF SILENT PRAYER...? TO THANK THE LORD FOR OUR SAFE RETURN FROM THE STARS.

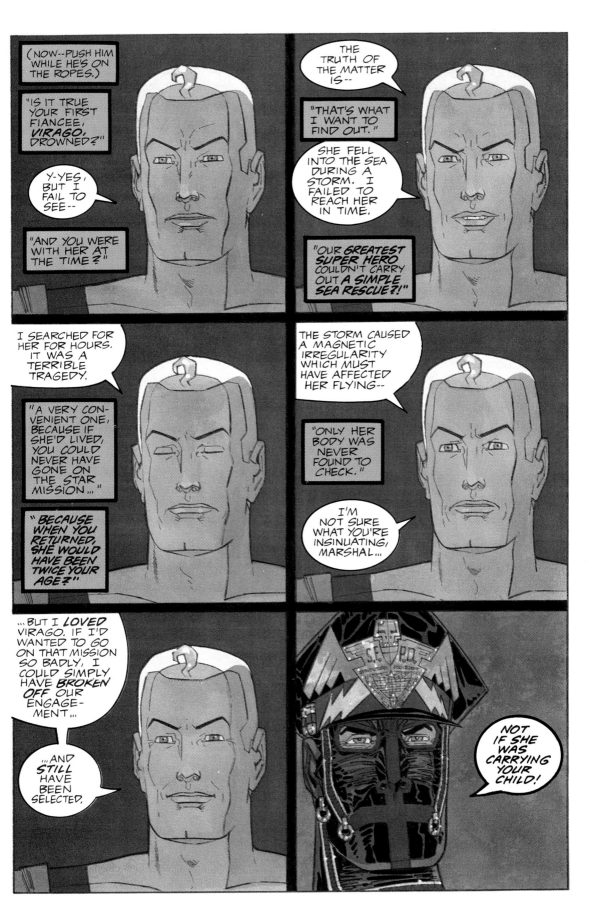

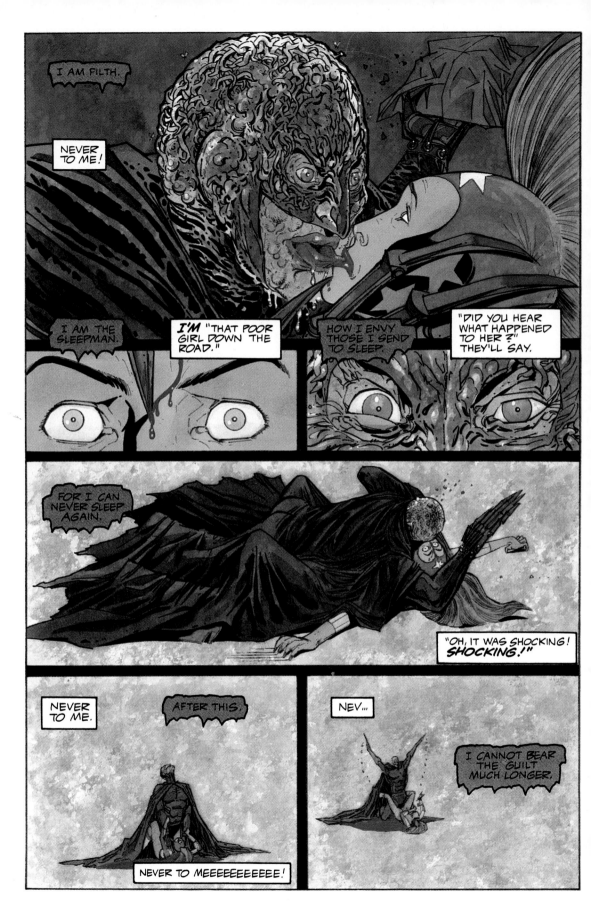

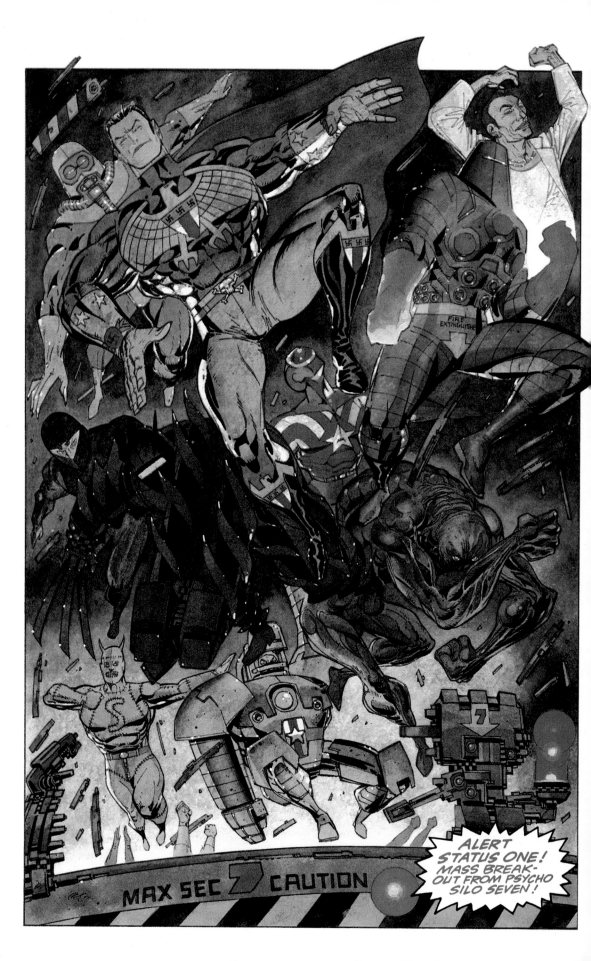

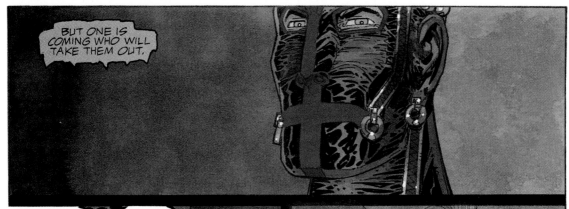

BUT ONE IS COMING WHO WILL TAKE THEM OUT.

SLEEPMAN... LET *THE LOONS* OUT...

WHAT'D HE LOOK LIKE?

LIKE HE NEEDED CLEARASIL REAL BAD.

CAPE?

MORE LIKE A TRASH BAG.

GIRL HE DID'S OVER THERE...

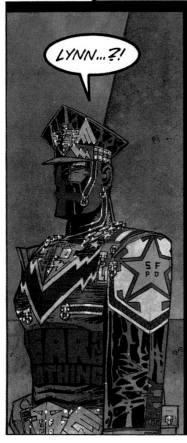

LYNN...?!

LYNN...

HE WILL HUNT ME DOWN NOW.

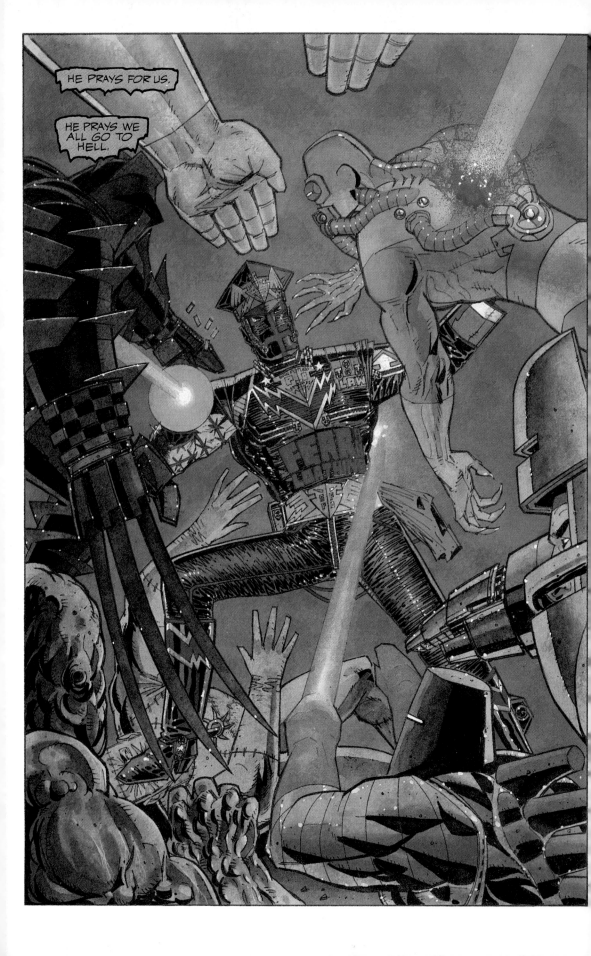

"Kennedy appointed a counterinsurgency expert, General Edward Lansdale, to coordinate the CIA's covert activities within the Departments of State and Defense. One of Lansdale's suggestions for overthrowing Castro was to spread the suggestion throughout Cuba that the second coming of Christ was imminent and that Christ opposed the anti-Christ Castro. A specific date was to be given for the Coming and on that date an American submarine would surface at night and set off starshells to manifest Christ's arrival. In theory, the Cubans would have risen against their leader."

—*CIA by Brian Freemantle, page 156*
Rainbird Publishers, 1983.
Copyright © Brian Freemantel 1983.
Reproduced by permission of
Rainbird Books, Ltd.

MARSHAL LAW

CHAPTER THREE
SUPER HERO MESSIAH

THE ZONE WAS
A JUST WAR.

GOD WAS ON
OUR SIDE.

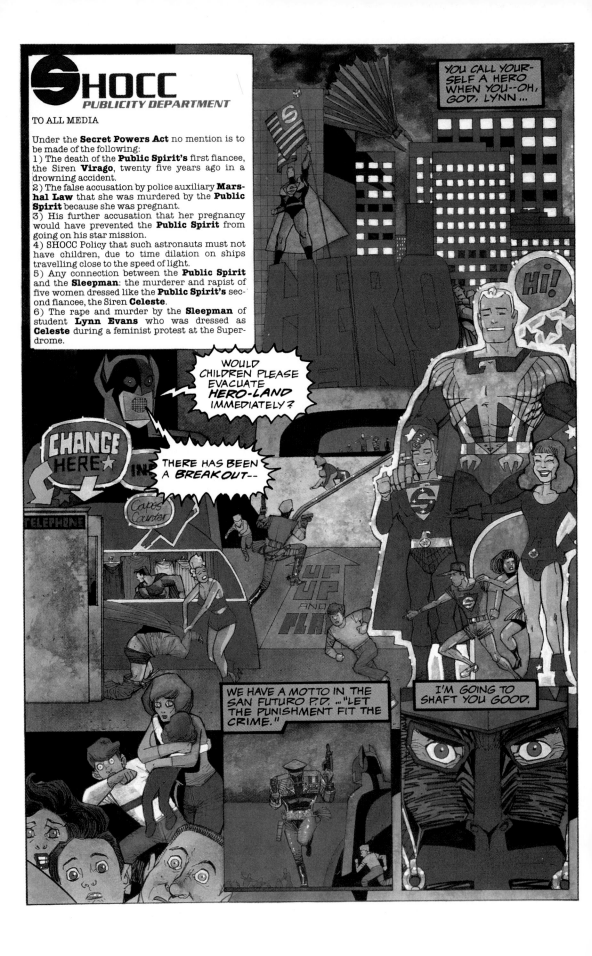

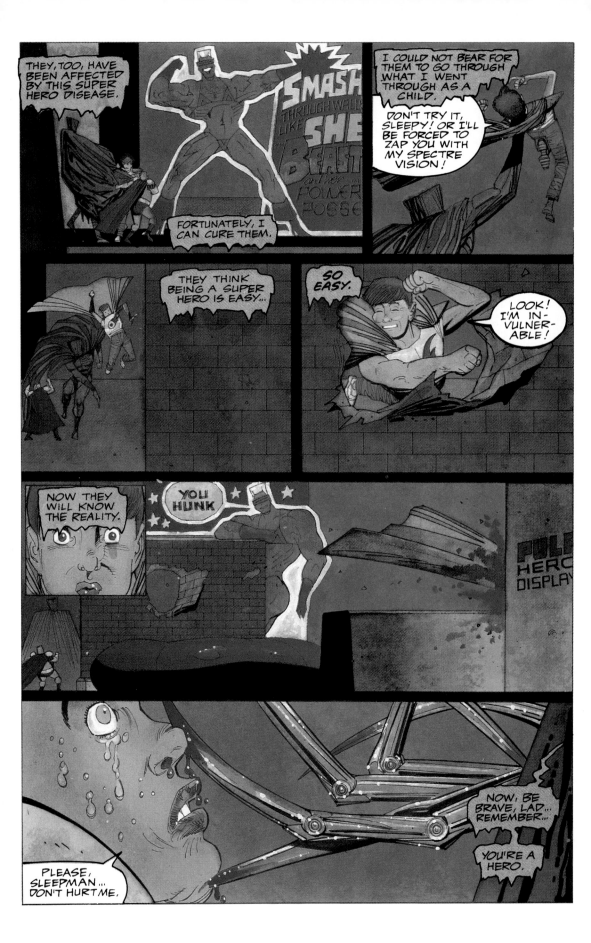

I'M AS HAPPY AS A **ba**STARD ON FATHERS DAY

BUT HER PARENTS WERE RIGHT. I WAS ON SOMETHING ALL RIGHT.

PURE HATE.

ANY NEWS ON THE LOONS?

THEY ARRESTED *SCAPEGOAT*. HE CONFESSED TO BEING THE SLEEPMAN.

WANTED TO KNOW IF HE'D DONE ENOUGH TO GO TO THE CHAIR.

I'LL PUT IN A GOOD WORD. HOW ABOUT *SLUG FEST?*

NOTHING SO FAR. BUT WITH HIS *PERSONAL HABITS*, WE SHOULD PICK HIM UP SOON.

JUST FOLLOW THE COW PATS.

JUDAS PHONE AGAIN?

TWICE.

ASKED THE USUAL PRICE FOR TELLING US WHERE *HITLER* IS HIDING.

DOES HE KNOW THE COST OF SILVER THESE DAYS?

OFF

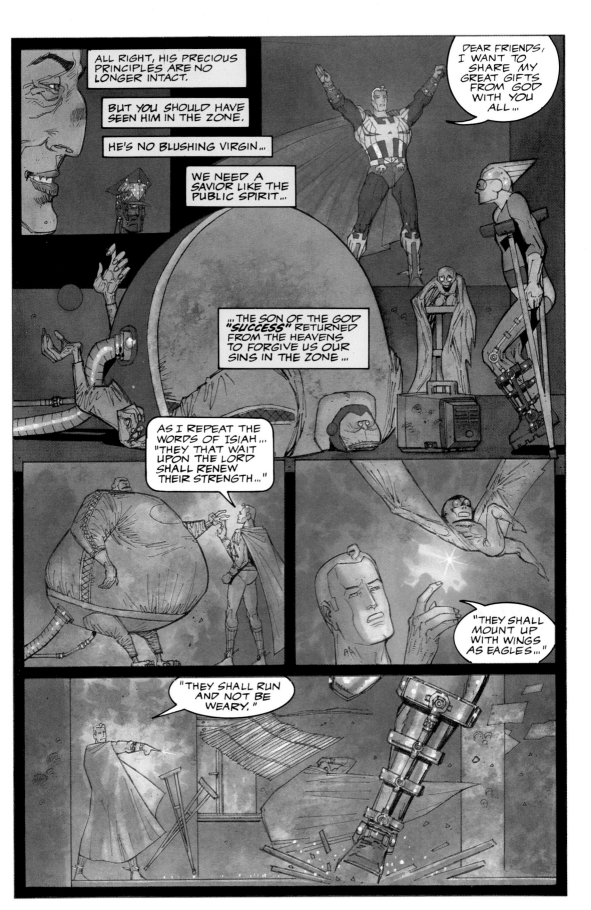

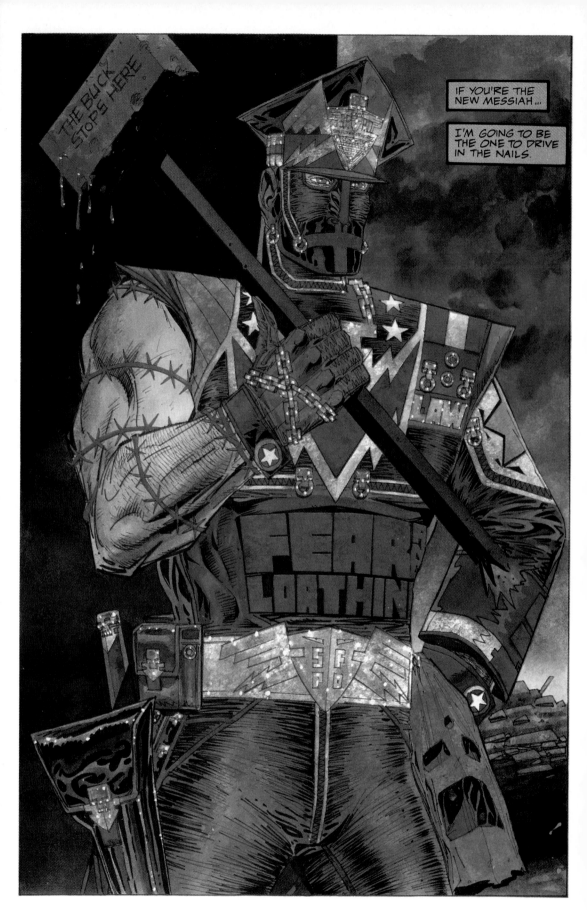

"So leap with joy, be blithe and gay,
Or weep, My friends, with sorrow,
What California is today,
The rest will be tomorrow."
—Richard Armour

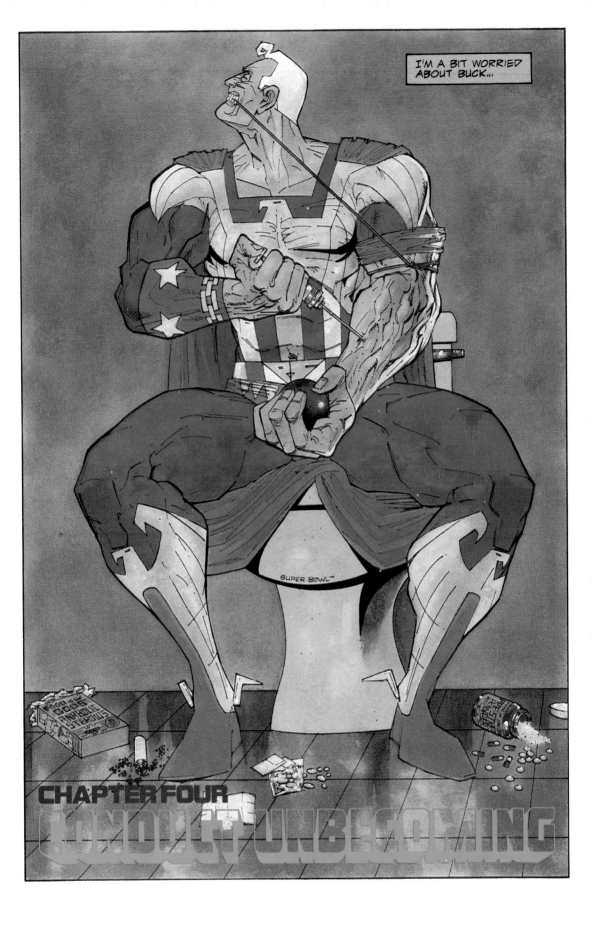

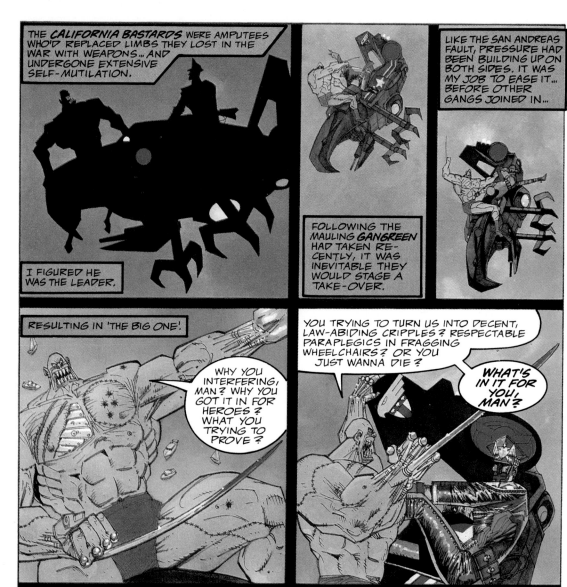

THE *CALIFORNIA BASTARDS* WERE AMPUTEES WHO'D REPLACED LIMBS THEY LOST IN THE WAR WITH WEAPONS... AND UNDERGONE EXTENSIVE SELF-MUTILATION.

I FIGURED HE WAS THE LEADER.

LIKE THE SAN ANDREAS FAULT, PRESSURE HAD BEEN BUILDING UP ON BOTH SIDES. IT WAS MY JOB TO EASE IT... BEFORE OTHER GANGS JOINED IN...

FOLLOWING THE MAULING *GANGREEN* HAD TAKEN RECENTLY, IT WAS INEVITABLE THEY WOULD STAGE A TAKE-OVER.

RESULTING IN 'THE BIG ONE'!

WHY YOU INTERFERING, MAN? WHY YOU GOT IT IN FOR HEROES? WHAT YOU TRYING TO PROVE?

YOU TRYING TO TURN US INTO DECENT, LAW-ABIDING CRIPPLES? RESPECTABLE PARAPLEGICS IN FRAGGING WHEELCHAIRS? OR YOU JUST WANNA DIE?

WHAT'S IN IT FOR YOU, MAN?

I'M IN IT FOR THE ENERGY!

DON'T TELL ME. HIS SHIP PASSED THROUGH A RADIOACTIVE CLOUD.?

NO. HE'S TAKING ANABOLIC STEROIDS.

IT'S ABOUT THE PUBLIC SPIRIT. I THINK I HAVE A FURTHER EXPLANATION FOR HIS DEGENERATE LIFESTYLE, LINKING HIM WITH THE MURDERS.

IT STRIKES ME AS TOTALLY RIDICULOUS HE SHOULD HAVE SO MUCH ATTENTION AND ACCLAIM WHEN HE OWES IT ALL TO A NEEDLE.

I WONDER WHEN HIS FANS ARE RAVING ABOUT HIM IF THEY EVER GIVE A MOMENT'S THOUGHT TO HOW HE LOOKS SO GOOD. I DON'T SUPPOSE THEY DO.

I DON'T SUPPOSE THEY'D CARE, EITHER. IN THEIR EYES THE GREAT PUBLIC SPIRIT CAN DO NO WRONG.

SHIT...

ALTHOUGH I WONDER IF FATHER O'BRIAN FOUND OUT. HE'S PULLED OUT OF THE WEDDING NOW. HE WON'T HAVE ANYTHING TO DO WITH HIM.

GROWTH HORMONES ... THYROID SUPPLEMENTATION ... ANDROGENICS... AMINO ACIDS...

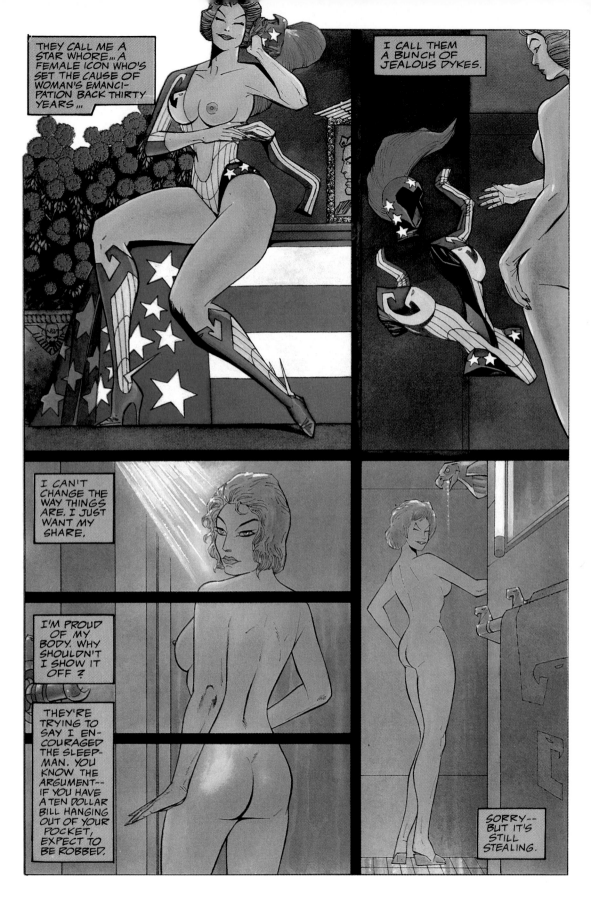

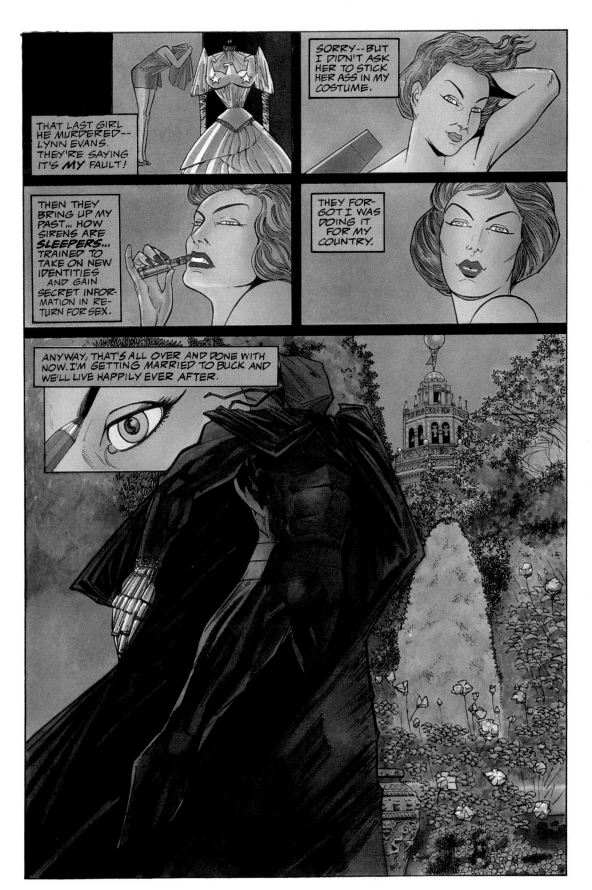

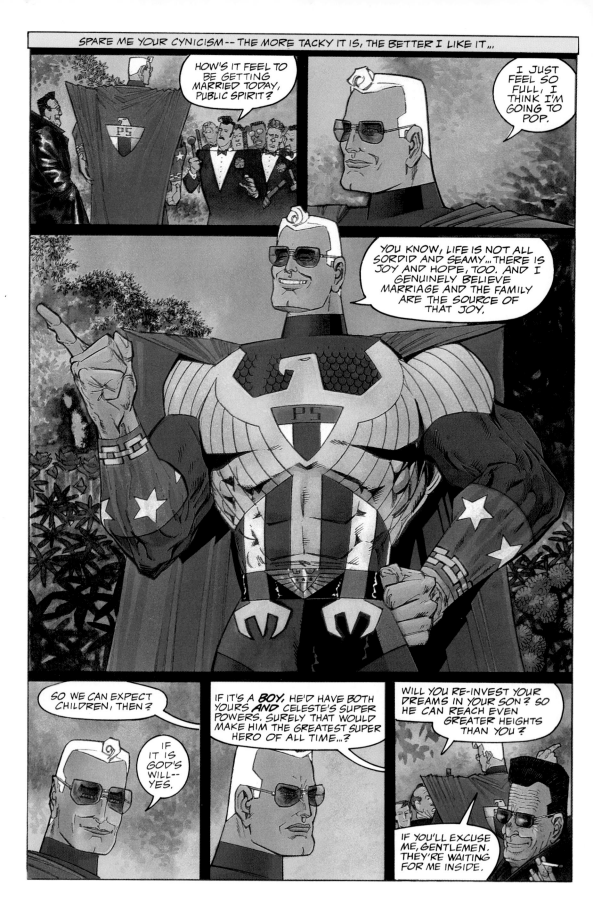

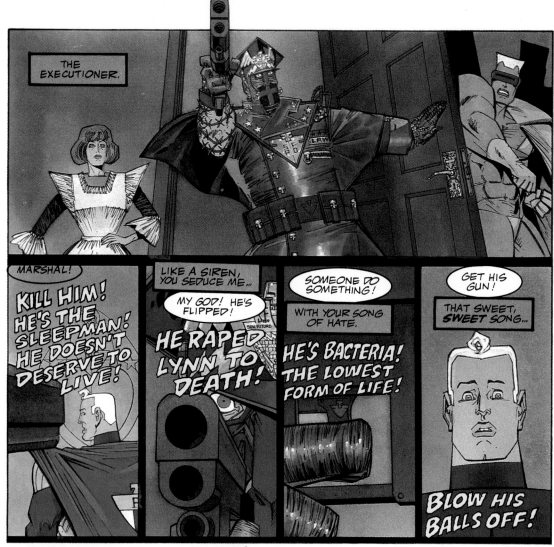

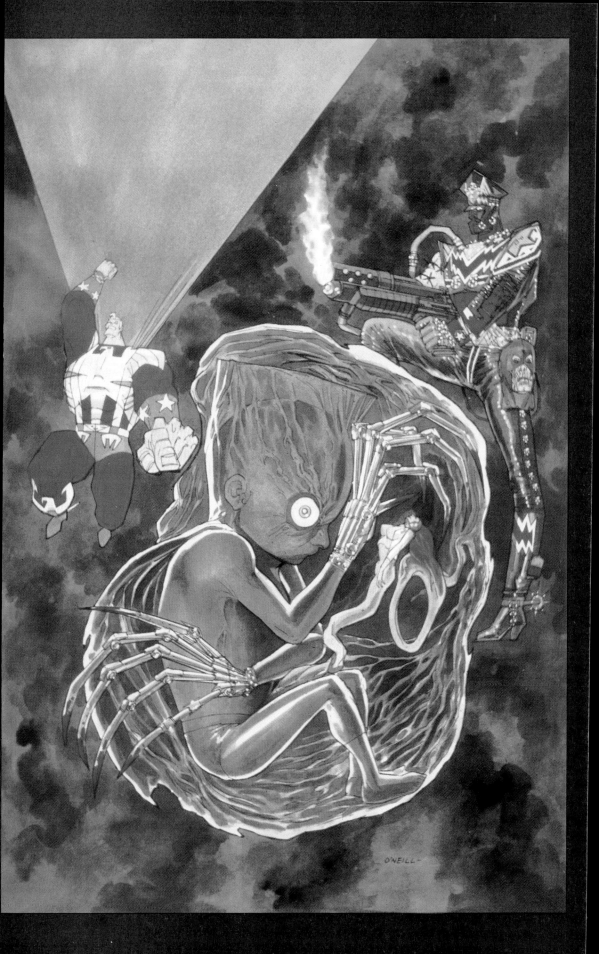

Cursed be the day of my birth! A time for cursing
it was, not for blessing, when my mother brought
me onto the world... Why did he not slay me yet
unborn, the womb for my tomb, and frustrate my
mother's hope Eternal? Why must I come out
into the light of day where only labor and sorrow
greet me?

—Jeremiah, Chapter 20, verses 14-18

THE WEDDING, I THINK YOU'LL AGREE, WAS A DISAPPOINTMENT. I'D CONCEALED MYSELF IN THE BUSHES AND WAS LOOKING FORWARD TO WATCHING YOU SHOOT *COLONEL BUCK CAINE, THE PUBLIC SPIRIT.*

AS IT TURNED OUT, THOUGH, YOU GUESSED MOTHER'S PLAN. SHE REVEALED HERSELF TO BE *VIRAGO* AND MADE A BREAK FOR IT, CLOSELY FOLLOWED BY MY FATHER.

YOU CAME OUT MOMENTS LATER, YELLING SOMETHING. THERE WAS A LOT OF SHOUTING INSIDE, SO I COULDN'T QUITE CATCH IT, BUT I THINK IT WAS *"BASTARDS!"*

AS YOU KNOW, YOU THEN CHECKED THE GUESTS' CASAS, IN CASE THEY WERE HIDING INSIDE.

YOU SEEMED TO BE IN RATHER A BAD MOOD.

IN FACT, EVERYONE WAS AT THE WEDDING EXCEPT FOR *ASSASSIN BUG, KOMA* AND *MASKARA* BETTING ON THE OUTCOME OF A FIGHT BETWEEN *THE SPOOK* AND *THE SURVIVALIST.*

FIVE HUNDRED DOLLARS THE SPOOK LOSES A PINT OF BLOOD.

YOU'RE ON!

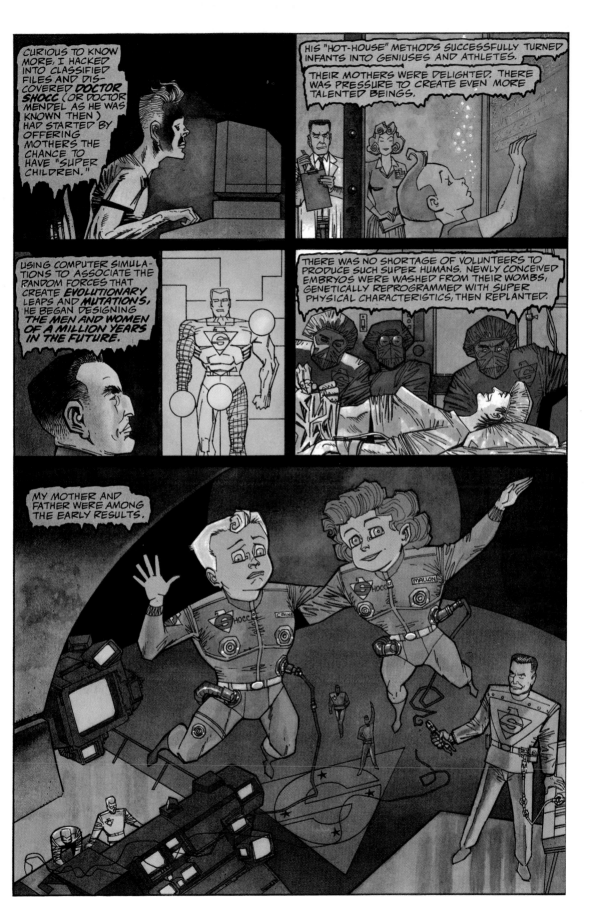

CURIOUS TO KNOW MORE, I HACKED INTO CLASSIFIED FILES AND DISCOVERED *DOCTOR SHOCC* (OR DOCTOR MENDEL AS HE WAS KNOWN THEN) HAD STARTED BY OFFERING MOTHERS THE CHANCE TO HAVE "SUPER CHILDREN."

HIS "HOT-HOUSE" METHODS SUCCESSFULLY TURNED INFANTS INTO GENIUSES AND ATHLETES.

THEIR MOTHERS WERE DELIGHTED. THERE WAS PRESSURE TO CREATE EVEN MORE TALENTED BEINGS.

USING COMPUTER SIMULATIONS TO ASSOCIATE THE RANDOM FORCES THAT CREATE *EVOLUTIONARY* LEAPS AND *MUTATIONS*, HE BEGAN DESIGNING *THE MEN AND WOMEN OF A MILLION YEARS IN THE FUTURE.*

THERE WAS NO SHORTAGE OF VOLUNTEERS TO PRODUCE SUCH SUPER HUMANS. NEWLY CONCEIVED EMBRYOS WERE WASHED FROM THEIR WOMBS, GENETICALLY REPROGRAMMED WITH SUPER PHYSICAL CHARACTERISTICS, THEN REPLANTED.

MY MOTHER AND FATHER WERE AMONG THE EARLY RESULTS.

OH, BOY... HUUH! ... I THOUGHT I'D SEEN EVERY- THING... HUUH! IT'S BAD FOR BUSINESS, I KNOW, BUT...

HA HA HA HA HA HA

THE REST OF IT YOU KNOW... HOW WE BLAMED THE MURDERS ON MY FATHER, BECAUSE OF OUR BIOLOGI- CAL SIMILARITIES.

USED YOUR HATRED OF HIM TO HOUND AND TORMENT HIM.

DO YOU GO AROUND WITH A BAG OVER YOUR HEAD RAPING WOMEN?

YOU HATED HIM SO MUCH, WE ALMOST GOT YOU TO KILL HIM FOR US.

I FELT TERRIBLE ABOUT INVOLVING YOU, BUT MOTHER INSISTED.

I WANTED TO CON- FESS ABOUT A DOZEN TIMES, BUT YOU NEVER GAVE ME THE CHANCE-- ALTHOUGH THAT'S UNDERSTANDABLE BECAUSE YOU WERE ALWAYS VERY BUSY.

ANYWAY, ENOUGH OF THIS! BACK TO THE PRESENT... MOTHER AND FATHER ARE HERE, TOO, AND I EXPECT YOU'LL BE ALONG SHORTLY AND IT'LL ALL END IN TEARS.

I REMEMBER YOU TOLD ME ONCE THAT LYNN WAS DOING A STUDY OF THE HERO AS A ROLE MODEL. I EXPECT SHE COULD HAVE GIVEN THE SCIENTIFIC EXPLANATION FOR MY BEHAVIOR.

SOMETHING TO DO WITH THE OEDIPUS COMPLEX, I IMAGINE: THE DESIRE BY A MALE CHILD TO POSSESS HIS MOTHER AND DESTROY HIS RIVAL, HIS FATHER.

A DILEMMA FINALLY RESOLVED BY HIS IDENTIFYING WITH HIS FATHER, TAKING ON HIS MORALS.

I MAY JUST BE PLAIN IGNORANT, BUT PERSONALLY I CAN'T SEE THE POINT OF SUCH ANALYSIS.

IT SEEMS TO ME THE PROBLEM LIES WITH MY PARENTS.

THEY SHOULD NOT HAVE BROUGHT ME INTO THIS WORLD... I DID NOT **ASK** TO BE BORN.

THEY CREATED ME-- A FRANKENSTEIN'S MONSTER-- DURING A NIGHT OF PLEASURE...

...LEAVING ME TO FACE A LIFETIME OF MISERY.

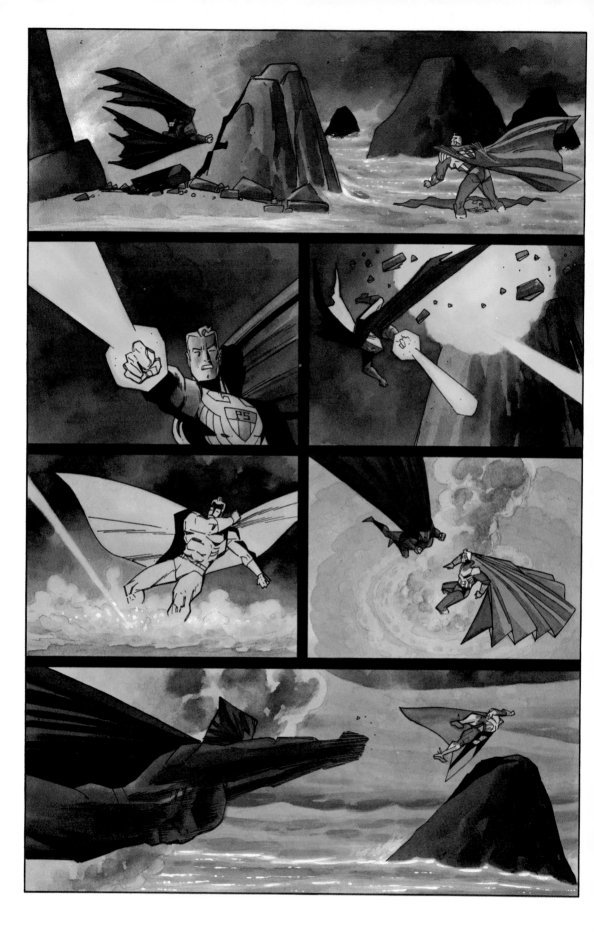

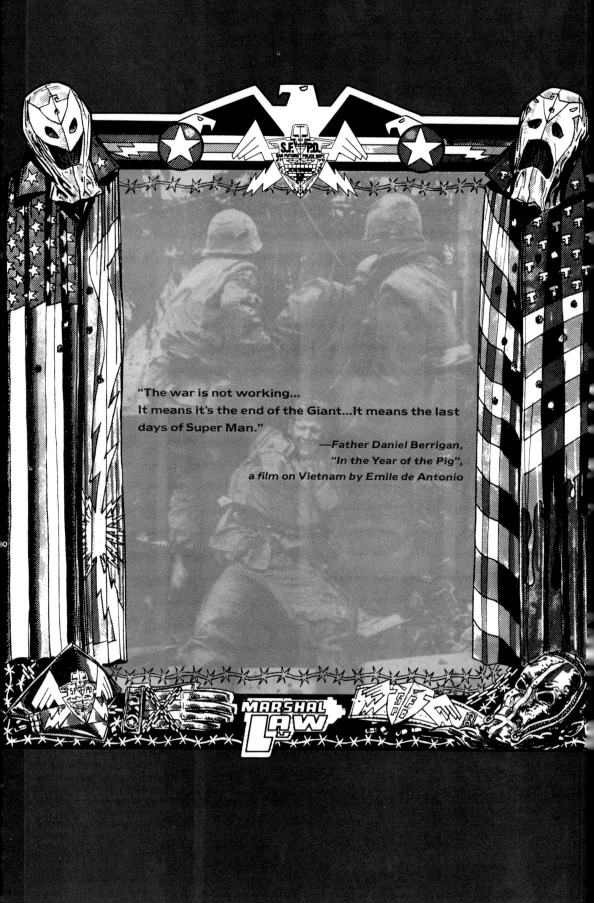

"The war is not working...
It means it's the end of the Giant...It means the last
days of Super Man."

—Father Daniel Berrigan,
"In the Year of the Pig",
a film on Vietnam by Emile de Antonio

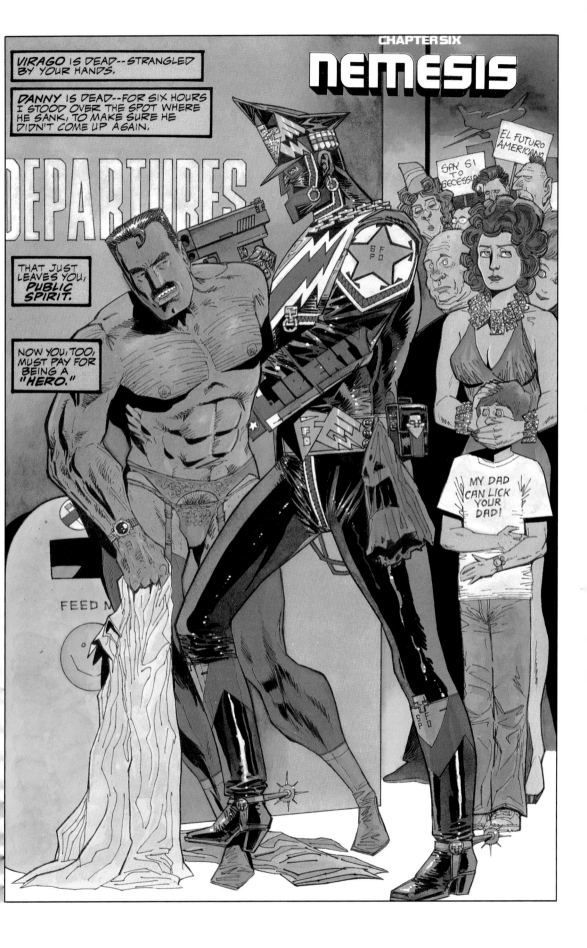

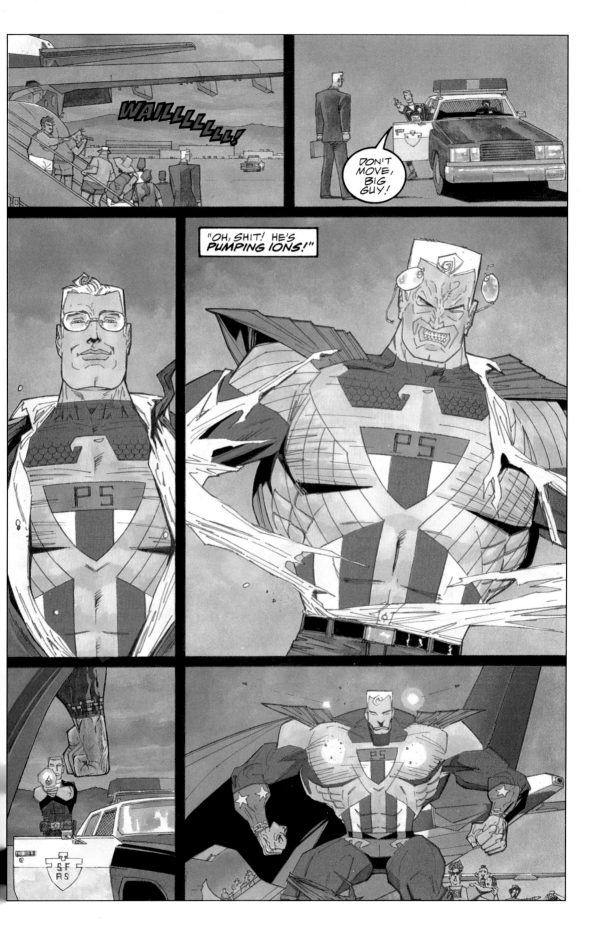

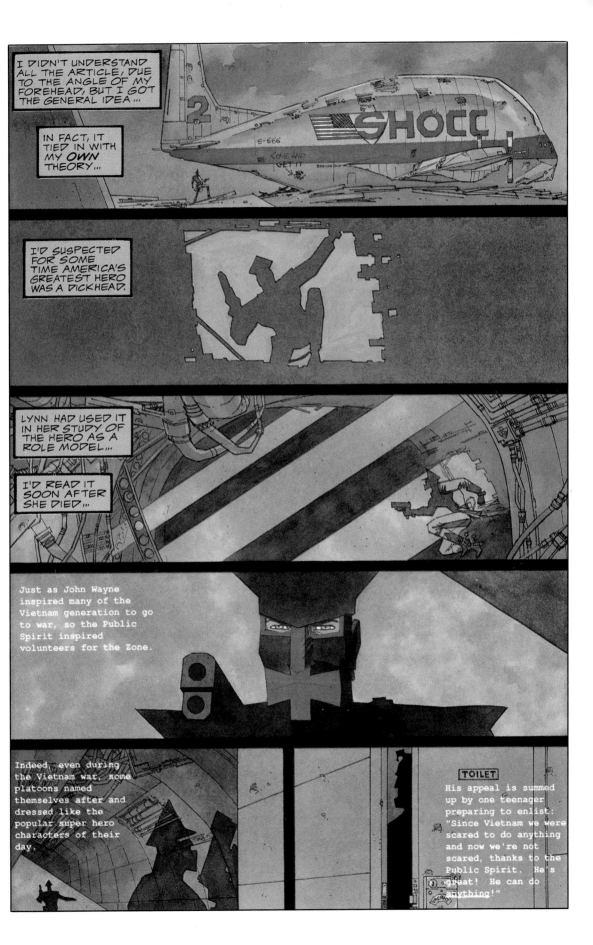

I DIDN'T UNDERSTAND ALL THE ARTICLE, DUE TO THE ANGLE OF MY FOREHEAD, BUT I GOT THE GENERAL IDEA ...

IN FACT, IT TIED IN WITH MY *OWN* THEORY ...

I'D SUSPECTED FOR SOME TIME AMERICA'S GREATEST HERO WAS A DICKHEAD.

LYNN HAD USED IT IN HER STUDY OF THE HERO AS A ROLE MODEL ...

I'D READ IT SOON AFTER SHE DIED ...

Just as John Wayne inspired many of the Vietnam generation to go to war, so the Public Spirit inspired volunteers for the Zone.

Indeed, even during the Vietnam war, some platoons named themselves after and dressed like the popular super hero characters of their day.

TOILET

His appeal is summed up by one teenager preparing to enlist: "Since Vietnam we were scared to do anything and now we're not scared, thanks to the Public Spirit. He's great! He can do anything!"

The myth and reality of the hero are sharply exposed by comparing two examples from the popular culture of the time: The Public Spirit bubble gum cards and the now notorious Zone Cards.

The Public Spirit cards, painted in bright, optimistic, primary colors, make his feats seem easy and attractive to children. There is no attempt at realism.

1 CONQUERING THE STARS

7 NO MORE SLUMS

15 RESCUING A NUN

16 RESCUING A DOG

17 RESCUING AN ORPHAN

18 A JOB WELL DONE

The term "Conquering" the stars is typical. Everything is seen as an object to be dominated (screwed). The objects of his domination are invariably members of the "weaker" female sex, children or animals. In the set of 55 cards, we never see him rescue a hunky male as this might suggest a dangerous homosexual ("weak" female) tendency. Note the phallic symbols: the sky-scraper, train and tornado.

In·the Zone Cards we see the result of these subliminal signals as heroes imitate their role model in "Shocc Treatment". While in "Siamese Twins"-- featuring genuine mutants, the tragic result of defoliants dumped on the jungle (to conquer/rape it)-- there is further proof that it's the victims, not the rapists who are the real heroes.

Throughout, the enemy, as well as the Shocc trooper--when he, too, is a victim--are shown sympatheticaly, unlike a previous series of cards where the Vietcong were portrayed as shifty, Asiatic sub-humans.

HOME FOR CHRISTMAS

AFTER THE BATTLE

DESTROYING A DOG

SIAMESE TWINS

SUPER ROULETTE

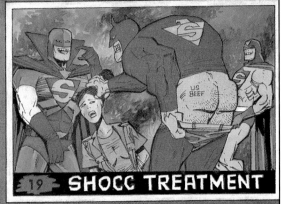

SHOCC TREATMENT

Particularly controversial were "Destroying a Dog" (paying tribute to the equally notorious "Mars Attacks" cards) and "Super Roulette" which repeats the claim in award-winning reporter John Pilger's book "Heroes" that the original "Russian Roulette" scene in "The Deer Hunter", which shocked movie-goers, was of dubious authenticity and was only inserted after the film's British backers rejected the original treatment as being uncommercial...

Not surprisingly, the cards--produced by students--were condemned as "tasteless" and "offensive"--e.g. they showed the truth.

EVERY TIME I HAD A DOLLAR, I'D RUSH OUT AND GET A PACK OF PUBLIC SPIRIT BUBBLE GUM CARDS WITH ITS FREE SHOCC BADGE.

I'D NEVER SWAP *HIM* FOR "BASEBALL STARS" OR "THE GREAT LIZARDS".

NOT EVEN FOR THE ONE WHERE THE DARK STAR NEMESIS DESTROYED THE DINOSAURS.

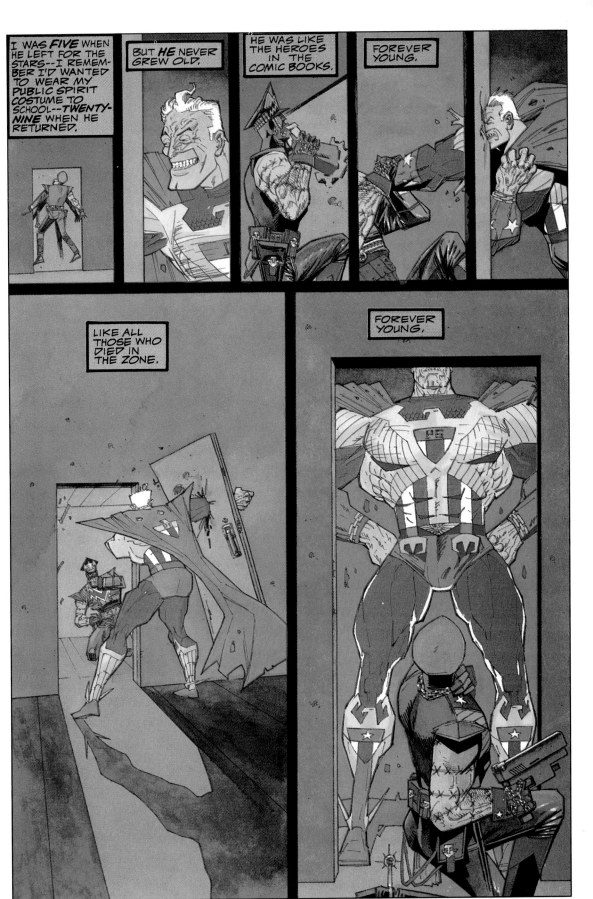

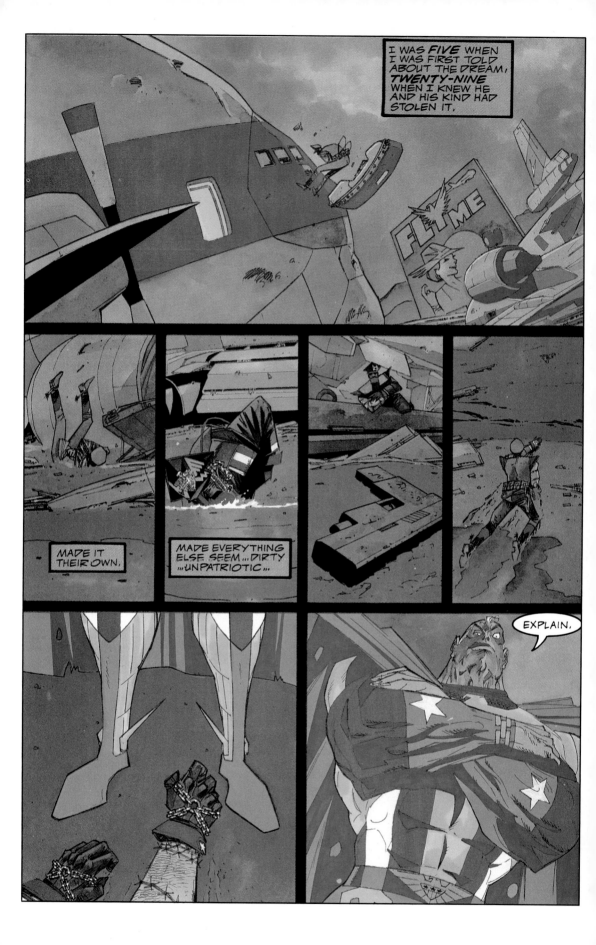

SPREADING *PERVERSION!*

HE COULD REPEL METAL BULLETS-- BUT NOT A PLASTIC FEAR GAS CAPSULE...

HOW MANY HAVE BEEN UP YOUR SECRET TUNNEL?

TROUBLE WITH FEAR, YOU NEVER KNOW HOW PEOPLE WILL REACT TO IT...

WELL, I'M GONNA PUT A STOP TO ONE PERVERT!

WHATEVER YOUR FEAR IS, THE NEURO-TOXIN SEEKS IT OUT... MAKES YOU FACE IT.

HIS WAS FEAR OF FAILING...

AND HE HAD.

SOON AS YOU GET A CLEAR SHOT, TAKE HIM OUT.

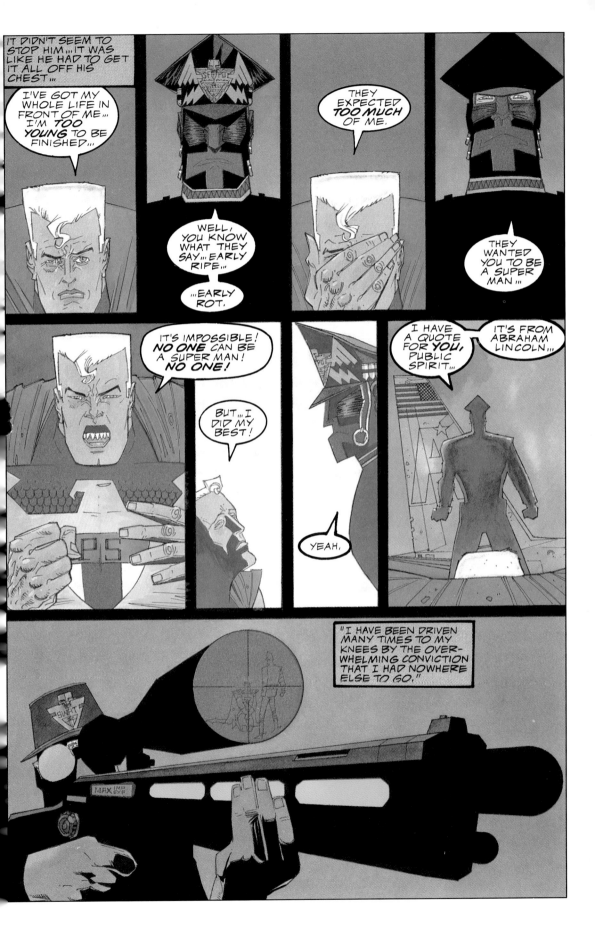

As optimism about the future gives way to pessimism, so hero is replaced by anti-hero. Of them all, the most brutal is "Marshal Law". With razor slashes down each cheek, looking as if his throat's been cut, his costume seems deliberately designed to be the exact opposite of the Public Spirit's.

He is the Public Spirit's Nemesis. The Sun Hero's Dark Twin. Just as Nemesis is believed to have caused the extinction of the dinosaurs, so he deals with "heroes" whose time has gone.

He is the Dark Star.

With his costume openly advertising his "hardness", such a man seems incapable of gentleness...of love...

GOODBYE, LYNN.

And yet, there are contradictions...is the barbed wire wrapped around his arm a sign of sado-masochistic practices? Or of a subconscious desire to be punished for his past crimes?

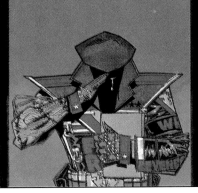

Only time will tell what kind of role model he will be, but if the past belongs to the Public Spirit...the future belongs to Marshal Law...

I'M A HERO HUNTER. I HUNT HEROES. HAVEN'T FOUND ANY YET.